AFTER HOURS JAZZ

BOOK 1

FOR PIANO SOLO

WRITTEN AND ARRANGED BY
PAM WEDGWOOD

FABER *ff* MUSIC

© 2007 by Faber Music Ltd
This edition first published in 2007
Bloomsbury House 74–77 Great Russell Street London WC1B 3DA
Music processed by Jackie Leigh
Cover by Velladesign
Printed in England by Caligraving Ltd

ISBN10: 0-571-52908-9
EAN13: 978-0-571-52908-7

To buy Faber Music publications or to find out about the full range of titles available
please contact your local retailer or Faber Music sales enquiries:

Faber Music Limited, Burnt Mill, Elizabeth Way, Harlow, CM20 2HX England
Tel: +44 (0)1279 82 89 82   Fax: +44 (0)1279 82 89 83
sales@fabermusic.com   fabermusic.com

CONTENTS

I GOT RHYTHM

Music and Lyrics by
George Gershwin and Ira Gershwin

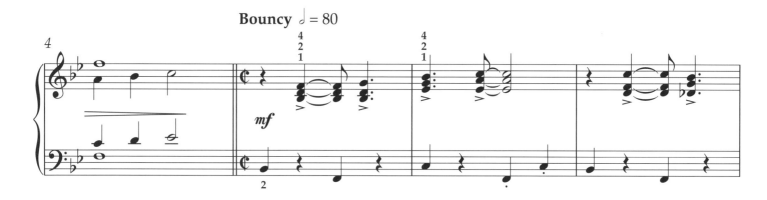

poco rit.

SAVE IT ALL FOR ME!

Pam Wedgwood

MY FAVORITE THINGS

Lyrics by Oscar Hammerstein II
Music by Richard Rodgers

IN THE STILL OF THE NIGHT

Words and Music by Cole Porter

LET THERE BE LOVE

Words by Ian Grant
Music by Lionel Rand

DE ROSA

Pam Wedgwood

THE PINK PANTHER THEME

With mystery ♩ = 104

Music by Henry Mancini

AUTUMN LEAVES

Words by Jacques Prevert
Music by Joseph Kosma
English Translation by Johnny Mercer

With a romantic feel ♩ = 84

Slow relaxed tempo

A FOGGY DAY

Music and Lyrics by
George Gershwin and Ira Gershwin

PAPER TIGERS

Pam Wedgwood

THEY CAN'T TAKE
THAT AWAY FROM ME

Music and Lyrics by
George Gershwin and Ira Gershwin

I'VE GOT YOU UNDER MY SKIN

Words and Music by Cole Porter

FLY ME TO THE MOON
(IN OTHER WORDS)

Words and Music by Bart Howard

LAURA

Words by Johnny Mercer
Music by David Raksin

AFTER HOURS

Alarm clocks, barking dogs, telephones, meetings and rush hour ... the hustle and bustle of life. What better way to relax than to sit down at the piano, chill out and indulge yourself with music from Pam Wedgwood's *After Hours*?

With a variety of pieces in styles to suit any mood—sentimental ballads to cosy dinner jazz, wistful blues to cheerful, upbeat tunes—*After Hours* provides the perfect antidote to stress. So conjure up the dimly lit atmosphere of a jazz club, and relax with these lush harmonies and laid-back melodies ...